Tie Your Shoes!

ISBN 978-1-338-08968-4
SCHOLASTIC INC.

It's a beautiful weekend. Mickey can't wait to get some fresh air and try a few fun activities with his friends, Goofy, Minnie, Donald, and Daisy!

There's only one problem — they all need tightly tied shoes! Goofy could use some tying practice. Luckily, his pals are ready to help!

First, Mickey, Goofy, and Donald take a bike ride. Goofy doesn't want to get his shoelaces stuck in the wheels, so Mickey gives him some tying tips.

Follow Mickey's lead for terrifically tied shoes!

1. Make a tall loop out of one shoelace. It looks like a tall tree!

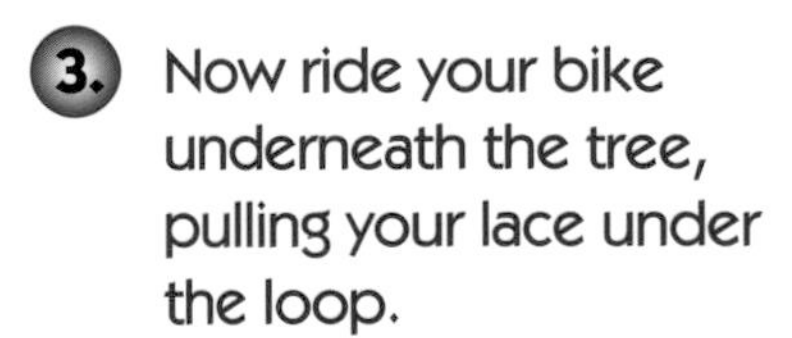

2. Pretend your other lace is a bike, and circle it around the bottom of the tree.

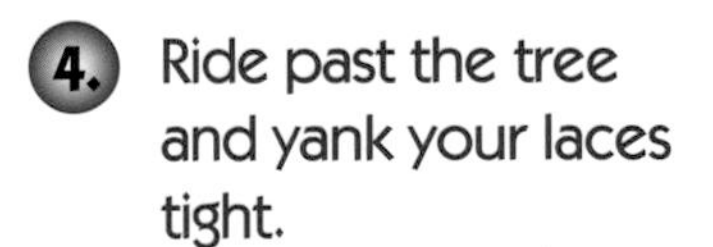

3. Now ride your bike underneath the tree, pulling your lace under the loop.

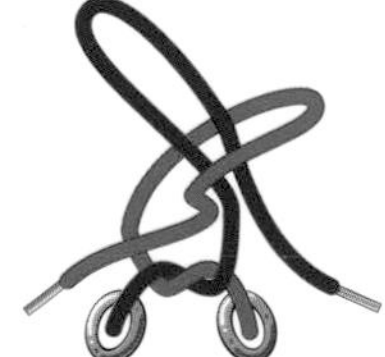

4. Ride past the tree and yank your laces tight.

NO GOOFING — YOU DID A GREAT JOB!

Next, Goofy, Mickey, and Minnie try roller-skating! Luckily, Minnie has a special method she uses to tie her skates. She learned it by practicing with some of her favorite bows — and she wants to teach Goofy!

Let Minnie show you her favorite way to tie shoes, skates, or even bows!

1. Make your laces into two big loops.

2. Cross the loops, forming an X.

3. Swoop one loop through the middle.

4. Tug both loops tight.

NOW YOU AND GOOFY ARE READY TO ROLL!

The next day, Goofy and his friends decide to have an obstacle course race — they'll run, dodge, and leap over different obstacles. Then they'll finish with a game of tug-of-war!

Before the race begins, Mickey helps Goofy find his sneakers and shows him another way to tie them. If Goofy's team is going to win, he doesn't want to trip and fall!

Try Mickey's mouse-tastic tying tips for yourself!

1. Make a loop with each shoelace. Make sure the ends of the loops are on opposite sides!

2. Place the loops side by side.

3. Pull each loop through the other loop.

4. Tug the ends tight, just like in a game of tug-of-war!

ON YOUR MARK, GET SET, GO!

It's a close race, but Goofy's team wins! He couldn't have done it without help from his friends. He wants to do something special to thank them — but what?

“Surprise!” Goofy cries a few hours later. He’s thrown a picnic party for all his pals — even Donald’s nephews! — with lots of yummy treats, balloons, and some thank-you presents.

Goofy winks at Minnie. “I tied the bows on the presents myself!” he says with a laugh.

When Goofy's friends open their gifts, they each find a brand-new pair of shoelaces inside. It's the perfect ending to a perfect weekend!